The Poker Was Framed!

**Story & Illustrations
by Danie Connolly**

Absolutely Perfect Publishing
139 Summer Street, Kennebunk, ME 04043

Designed by Aikman Design

ISBN number 978-0-9970546-0-6

Summary:
  Within the confines of the living room,
   a table lamp defends an accused
    fireplace poker of committing
     a dastardly crime, despite
      the ironclad testimony
      from a key witness.

"How you do with what you have is who you are."

Much love to my all my grandchildren from GranDanie.
Always be kind and you'll always be happy.

To BBB, Thanks for being the string
to my balloon . . . Sweet Dan

The Shade had drawn a dark, dark tale
of how the Ming was maimed.
Someone was the culprit, but. . .
who could they blame?

Resting in the corner
sporting a faulty face,
stood the assumed accused
with the must-be-guilty fate.
"Why me?" moaned the Poker,
his deadpanned face chagrinned.

"I'm innocent, I tell you!
Being a Poker's my only sin."

The Ming Vase couldn't say for sure
what villain she could name.
And thus began the trial of
the Poker who was framed!

The jury was selected,
Twelve Pillows would hear the case.

Two eager legal Lamps opposed,
perched ready from their base.

Grandfather Clock presided.
As a judge, he had no peers.
The hands of justice wound around
with wisdom through the years.

The Dictionary testified
because of all she knew,
but A to K and L to Z
could not find a clue.

"I witnessed the entire thing,"
the Rug began to brag.
"From where I lay, the Poker played
a game of push and tag."

"He dinged the Ming!
He stoked and poked
until she tumbled to the floor!
He's stirred the ashes many times.
He's guilty . . . nothing more!"

"She toppled from so high!
It's a miracle at all...
She'd have smashed to smithereens,
if I didn't break her fall!"

"It's curtains for the Poker!"
The Drapes flapped instantly.
The Shutters muttered, "Open–shut!
There's no defense. Guilty!"

The Bells chimed in, "Oh, what a sin!"
The Plants rustled their leaves.
Commotion filled the courtroom.
"Order! Order! Please!"

The little Lamp stood solemnly
as he pled the Poker's case.
But those Cushions weren't persuaded
by the look on his 'guilty' face.

The Door declared, "This case is closed.
Let justice have her day."
The Doorknob nodded brashly.
"We wouldn't see it any other way!"

Suddenly a light clicked on.
The little Lamp began to beam.
"There's another side to this story,
the truth's not what it seems."

It took only a moment
to hover over to the stand.
"Tell us what you observed,"
he coaxed the Ceiling Fan.

The fan peered down and gazed around,
a sneer upon her face.
The blades revolved, increasing speed,
and hummed, "What a disgrace!"

"I saw it all from way above,"
the Fan began to testify.
"Such fabricated stories...
all from a Rug that lies!"

Above the Mantel Clock she snarled,
"A guilty verdict there should be...
You've struck one too many times!
Let's throw away your key!"

Up sprang the hands!
The Clock cried out in fright,
"The Vase just tumbled over
from a slight shove to the right!"

"It truly was an accident...
The Vase had blocked my view.
The ledge was closer than I thought.
Mings can't fly? Who knew?!"

The Ferns fumed!
The Screens screamed!
The Window whined in pain!
The Stairs stared!
The Mirror reflected,
"Was this trial in vain?"

The legal Lamps approached the bench.
"Your honor, we must say,
evidence in the Poker's defense
makes some sense today."

"From what we see, we must agree,
no criminal do we find.
A catastrophe? Most certainly!
But justice can't be blind."

Some say they saw the Poker smile.
Some even saw a grin.
Some heard a deep sigh of relief
from the Poker, nearly done in!

When you point your finger and
you're ready to show blame,
remember how very innocent was
the Poker who was framed!

Danie Connolly has always enjoyed the exuberance of little kids, spending over 40 years writing and illustrating children's storybooks, hoping to make them smile and giggle even more! Throughout her life, she has been thankful for the encouragement and support of family, lifelong friends, and wonderful people who have touched her life.

Danie was encouraged at an early age by her elementary teachers to pursue art, and she has been grateful for their confidence in her talent ever since. In the 7th grade, her cousin Vicki typed Danie's first children's story, and paved the way for a life of writing. By taking the kind words and sage advice from her peers to learn and succeed in the field of children's storybooks, her heart has always been filled with the joy of doing what she loves. Danie has taught art to Alzheimer's patients, painted wall murals for hospitals and created theatrical backdrops.

She is a photojournalist, and an award-winning playwright whose plays have been staged for children and adults throughout New England. She has also been a columnist for newspapers and magazines.

Absolutely Perfect Publishing created *Tubestories*, a line of children's storybooks and greeting cards based on some of the outrageous characters from her books. Danie Connolly resides on the southern Maine coast with her husband Bob and three very spoiled Scottish Terriers.

BOOKS BY DANIE CONNOLLY

A Hop, Skip and Jump, Jump, Jump!
Dum Dum Deedlebird
Everybody's Puppy – Nobody's Dog
Happy Birthday to U!
Loser Louis
On the Road to Life
Rainbow Junkyard
Ribbit
Snarls
Teardrop Stew
The Ants
The Bald Headed Eagle that Refused to be Bald
The Great Soapino
The Case of the Missing Sock
The Day Bradley Lost His Imagination
The Poker Was Framed!
The Silverware

HOLIDAY BOOKS

Heartseeds
The Littlest Christmas Tree
Miss L. Toes
Recycled Angels
The Reindeer Hop
Reindeer Sniffles
S.A.N.T.A.
The Great Christmas Cookie Escape
The Snowmen of Kindness
The Stained Glass Angel
The 13th Day of Christmas
The Third Turtle Dove
Twinkles
Red Lights
Thomas T. Turkey

51761035R00020